My Baptism Memories

Val Chadwick Bagley

Communications, Inc.

Published by Covenant Communications, Inc.
American Fork, Utah

Printed in China
First Printing: August 2004

10 09 08 07 10 9 8 7 6 5

ISBN 1-59156-552-9
ISBN 978-1-59156-552-9

(Photo)

This is the Baptism Journal of

____

Given with love

All About Me

My full name is ______________________________.

I was born on ______________________________

in ____________________(city)____________________(county)

______________________________(state).

The other people in my family are ______________________

____

____.

These are the things I like to do:

____

____

____

____.

I'm This Big!

I am __________ feet ____________ inches tall.

I weigh ______________________________ pounds.

My hair color is ______________________________.

My eye color is ______________________________.

I think I look most like my __________________.

This is how big my hand was
when I was baptized.
(Trace around your hand.)

My Parents

My father's name is________________________.

He is a________________________________.

What I like best about my dad is______________

____.

(Photo of My Father)

My mother's name is ________________________________.

Her maiden name is ________________________________.

She is really good at ________________________________.

What I like best about my mom is ____________________

____.

(Photo of My Mother)

My Grandparents

My father's parents are ______________________________

and ____.

What I like best about Grandma and Grandpa ___________

is ____.

Photo of My Grandparents (Father's Side)

My mother's parents are ________________________________

and ____.

What I like best about Grandpa and Grandma ____________

is ____

____.

Photo of My
Grandparents
(Mother's Side)

The Church

When I was baptized, the president of the Church was

____.

His counselors were ______________________________

and ____.

There were ________________________________ members of the Church throughout the world.

There were ______________ missionaries in the mission field.

When I was baptized I lived in the ____________________ Ward in the ____ Stake.

My primary teacher was ____________________.

My 8th Birthday

I turned eight years old on ____________________(date).

These are some of the things I did to celebrate my

eighth birthday: ____________________________________

____

____

____

____

____.

(Photo of eight-
year-old me)
Turning eight is great because: ____________________
____
____
____
____
____
____
____.
8

Interview with My Bishop

Bishop ______________________ interviewed me

on __________________________________ (date) at

_____________________________________ (place).

One thing we talked about was _______________

____

____

____.

My Bishopric

Bishop:____

First Counselor:______________________________________

Second Counselor:____________________________________

My Baptism Day

I was baptized on____________________________(date)

at____(where)

by____,

who holds the office of____________________________

in the__________________________________Priesthood.

(Photo of Me on
the Day of My
Baptism)

The weather was ____.

The water in the baptismal font was ____________________________.

My witnesses were

_________________________ and _______________________.

I especially remember _____________________________________

____

____.

My Baptism Program

The opening prayer was given by:

____

Talks were given by:

____

____

Musical numbers:

____

____

The closing prayer was given by:

____

What I especially liked about the program:

____

____

____

____

____

____

My Confirmation

I was confirmed a member of The Church of Jesus Christ

of Latter-day Saints on________________________________(date)

at____(place)

by____,

who holds the office of ______________________________ in the

Melchizedek Priesthood.

These are the names of the priesthood holders who stood

in the circle to confirm me a member of the Church:

____

____

____

These are some of my feelings on the day I was confirmed

a member of the Church:____________________________________

____

____.

Promises

(Mosiah 18:8–11)

By being baptized, I promise Heavenly Father that I will:

____

____.

Because of the promises I made through baptism,

Heavenly Father promises me that He will:

____

____.

My Testimony

Guests at My Baptism

Photographs

My Father's Testimony

My Mother's Testimony

My Grandparents' Testimonies